4

AND WAKING DOESN'T ALWAYS MAKE THINGS BETTER.

RACHEL--! I DON'T UNDER- STAND--

--THIS HAS TO BE A DREAM-- ONLY IT FEELS SO REAL.

AND THE X-MEN-- MORE PUPPETS THAN PEOPLE-- TRAVESTIES OF THE HEROES I REMEMBER.

WHEN THE REALITY NO LONGER EXISTS...

... EXPLOITERS CAN TAKE THE LEGEND...

...AND MAKE IT WHATEVER THEY WANT, GOOD OR BAD.

RACHEL! YOU'RE NOT IN THIS PRODUCTION!

YOU HAD YOUR CHANCE AT STARDOM, BABY PHOENIX, AND BLEW IT!

WHEN YOUR TEAMMATES NEEDED YOU MOST...

...YOU RAN OUT ON THEM!

MY MISTAKE--
--MY SHAME--

--BUT NOW I'VE A CHANCE...
...TO MAKE AMENDS.

NOT SO FAST, YOUNG LADY.

NOBODY LEAVES WITHOUT MY PERMISSION.

YOU CAN'T HOLD ME!

CARE TO BET YOUR LIFE ON THAT?

STOP IT!

PROFESSOR-- X-MEN--

--YOU'RE TEARING HER APART!!

6

SHE'S OUR *FRIEND!* IF SHE STAYS OR GOES, IT SHOULD BE BY HER FREE CHOICE!

IT'S WRONG TO FORCE HER!

AND I WON'T LET YOU--!

IF I CAN REACH RACHEL--TOUCH HER-- --MY POWER SHOULD *PHASE* HER THROUGH HER CHAINS--!

BLESS YOU, KITTY!

BE *SEEING* YOU--

--MAYBE SOONER THAN YOU THINK!

THAT, YOUNG LADY, WAS VERY *NAUGHTY!*

SURE SEEMED LIKE A GREAT IDEA...

...AT THE TIME.

AND I'M SURE YOU KNOW...

...WHAT HAPPENS TO NAUGHTY LITTLE GIRLS.

WARWOLVES! MANIFEST YOURSELVES-- --AND TEACH THE BRAT A LESSON!

NO!

THE WALL--!

I'M SOLID AGAIN-- I CAN'T PHASE--

--CAN'T ESCAPE-- --X-MEN--

--ALL MONSTERS--

NO KEEP AWAY DON'T NO PLEASE *NO!*

HOW'S MY BEST DRAGON?

HOW'S ABOUT A SCRATCH, CUTE-'UMS...

...IN YOUR FAVORITE SPOT...

...BETWEEN YOUR SHOULDER *BLAST AND DARNATION!*

FORGOT.

I'M NOT NORMAL ANYMORE, EVEN FOR AN X-MAN.

MY NATURAL STATE IS TO BE *PHASED*--

-- AS PHYSICALLY INTANGIBLE AS A GHOST--

--TO BECOME SOLID...

...I HAVE TO CONCENTRATE...

...HARD AS I CAN.

HOORAY!

BUT IT WON'T LAST LONG.

WHAT A MESS!

Oh, GOLLY-- I REMEMBER...

...I FELL ASLEEP...

...WITH THESE PICTURES IN MY ARMS.

ME AND PROFESSOR XAVIER, WHEN I'D JUST JOINED THE SCHOOL.

AND A TEAM SHOT...

...RIGHT BEFORE EVERYTHING FELL APART.

NOW, HE'S GONE, AWAY ACROSS THE UNIVERSE...

...PROBABLY NEVER TO RETURN.

AND THE *X-MEN*...

...THE X-MEN...

...ARE *DEAD!*

SHE'D BEEN SWIMMING ALONE, WHEN THE POD POPPED UP AND ASKED HER TO PLAY.

THE DOLPHINS' NATURAL EXUBERANCE WAS TOO INFECTIOUS...

...TO BE DENIED.

SHE KNEW NEXT TO NOTHING OF THE SEA.

SO THEY DELIGHTED IN TEACHING HER ITS WONDERS AND MYSTERIES.

SHE WAS HAVING SO MUCH FUN...

...SHE LOST ALL TRACK OF TIME.

UNTIL...

A BIRD OF FIRE...

...HERALDING THE SUNRISE!

HOW BEAUTI-FUL!

BUT HAVE I BEEN AWAY SO LONG?

FAREWELL, FINFRIENDS!

SEE YOU AGAIN SOON, I HOPE! UNTIL THEN, STAY WELL!!

I KNOW BRIAN WILL BE WORRIED.

PLEASE LET HIM NOT BE ANGRY.

HER NAME IS MEGGAN.

AND SHE IS AS MUCH A CREATURE OF THE EARTH...

...AS OF MAN.

IN OLDEN DAYS, SHE'D BE CALLED ONE OF THE FAERY FOLK.

ACTUALLY, THOUGH, SHE'S A MUTANT.

HOME, DARLING-DEAREST!

DID YOU...

...MISS ME?!

LIVING ROOM--TORN APART--

-- A BATTLE?!

BUT UPSTAIRS WAS UNTOUCHED, THE LIGHTHOUSE UNDAMAGED. NO SIGN OF INTRUDERS.

NOT AN ATTACK, THEN--

--SOMETHING WORSE.

BRITAIN'S MOST BEAUTIFUL WOMAN

Psylocke joins the X-MEN - Big Brother, wish me luck!

PICTURES-- OF BRIAN'S TWIN SISTER, BETSY--

--ALL STREWN ABOUT--

--THE TELLY?!

TO RECAP THE LATEST NEWS FROM AMERICA...

...THE MUTANT SUPER-TEAM KNOWN AS X-MEN...

HAS BEEN SLAIN IN DALLAS, TEXAS.

NO! Oh, NO!

IT CAN'T BE TRUE!!

AMONG THE FATALITIES, AN ENGLISH MUTANT KNOWN BY THE CODE-IDENTITY, PSYLOCKE.

OH, BRIAN-- MY POOR, SWEET LUV--

--THIS IS *TERRIBLE!*

NAH. COMES WITH THE COSTUME, DON'T'CHA KNOW?

SMELL. DRINK.

SO STRONG... ...MAKES ME ILL.

LOOK AT ME, MEG.

CAPTAIN BRITAIN! SOME HERO. COULDN'T EVEN SAVE...

...MY OWN SISTER.

BETSY AND THE X-MEN WERE HALF-A-WORLD AWAY, HOW COULD YOU HAVE POSSIBLY KNOWN SHE WAS IN DANGER?!

THAT'S THE POINT! WHAT THE BLAZES USE AM I IF I *DON'T* KNOW SUCH THINGS?!

BRIAN, SHE WAS A GROWN WOMAN.

SHE CHOSE HER LIFE-- *SHE'S* RESPONSIBLE FOR HER DECISIONS AND HER DEEDS--

--YOU'RE NOT TO BLAME.

THE DEVIL YOU SAY!

CHANGELING COW, WHAT DO YOU KNOW-- ABOUT *ANYTHING*-- YOU NEVER HAD A FAMILY, NEVER LOST ANYONE YOU CARED FOR!

GO *AWAY*, MEGGAN!

I DON'T WANT YOUR SYMPATHY.

I ONLY WANT TO BE LEFT ALONE.

DUMB... --TELEPORTED INSTINCTIVELY... ...SO DUMB--

...WHEN I GOT HIT--

--BAD MOVE!

FEEL SO WEAK--

--LIKE ALL I WANT TO DO...

...IS LIE DOWN AND DIE--

--MAY GET MY WISH!

WHERE ARE YOUR QUIPS NOW, SWASH-BUCKLER?

GET UP, GET UP--

--ALL YOU NEED DO TO SAVE YOURSELF...

...IS REACH THAT CONTROL PAN-- eh?!

SYSTEM SHORT-CIRCUITING!

IT'S KITTY-- PHASING THROUGH THE WALL!

NIGHTCRAWLER--

--oh, CRUMBS!?!

KLANG!

BLESS YOU, KATZCHEN.

YOU OKAY, NIGHT-CRAWLER?

JA-- THANKS TO YOUR TIMELY INTERVENTION.

GREAT-- THEN YOU MIND TELLING ME...

...WHAT THE HECK YOU THINK YOU WERE PLAYING AT HERE?!!

TESTING MYSELF.

15

A FULL-BORE COMBAT EXERCISE-- WITH THE SAFETY INTERLOCKS DISCONNECTED--

--SO SOON AFTER YOUR RELEASE FROM MOIRA'S HOSPITAL--

--ARE YOU *CRAZY?!*

LUCKY FOR YOU THE BACK-UP ALARMS...

...SOUNDED IN THE HOUSE THE MINUTE YOU STARTED.

I HAD TO LEARN, KITTY, IF I HAD LOST MY EDGE.

DOESN'T IT MATTER IF, IN THE PROCESS, YOU LOSE YOUR *LIFE?!*

WHAT GIVES, KURT-- YOU FEEL LEFT OUT BECAUSE THE REST OF THE X-MEN GOT KILLED AND WE DIDN'T?

YOU FIGURE ON THIS BEING THE PERFECT WAY TO CATCH UP TO 'EM??

YOU HAVE *NO RIGHT* TO SAY SUCH THINGS!

YOU HAVEN'T THE RIGHT TO GIVE ME A *CAUSE!*

JA. I KNOW. I'M SORRY.

WHEN I AWOKE FROM MY COMA, I WAS SO... *HAPPY* TO BE ALIVE. DEAR *KATZCHEN,* YOU CANNOT IMAGINE.

ALL I REMEMBERED WAS THE PAIN OF BEING WOUNDED-- AND THE NEXT THING I KNEW, I WAS HERE IN MOIRA MacTAGGART'S MUTANT RESEARCH FACILITY, AND IT WAS MONTHS LATER.

AND I THOUGHT, I'VE HAD A TASTE OF DEATH--BUT I SURVIVED. I BEAT THE REAPER!

MY TIME WILL COME-- BUT NOT TODAY!

I WANTED TO SHARE THAT JOY WITH THOSE I LOVED BEST-- YOU AND PETER AND LOGAN AND ORORO, WITH *ALL* THE X-MEN--

--ONLY I COULDN'T. BECAUSE THEY WERE DEAD.

I KNOW HOW YOU FEEL, KURT.

AND THEN, LAST NIGHT... ...I HAD THIS... *DREAM.*

SAY *WHAT?!?*

I'VE NEVER HAD THE LIKE.

WHEN IT WAS DONE, I FELT ASHAMED--ALMOST PHYSICALLY ILL.

I WAS IN A MOVIE STUDIO, WITH TWISTED, DECADENT VERSIONS OF THE X-MEN AS THE CAST, AND *HERR PROFESSOR XAVIER* OUR DIRECTOR.

AND *RACHEL* WAS THERE, TOO--

--SOME KIND OF PRISONER--

--AND YOU HELPED HER ESCAPE?

JAH! ONLY I WAS LEFT BEHIND...

...TO BEHOLD THE X-MEN'S TRANSFORMATION INTO MONSTERS.

THE PROF CALLED 'EM *WARWOLVES.*

YOU ALSO, THEN!

PRETTY WEIRD, *huh?*

IF WE BOTH HAD THE SAME EXPERIENCE, MAYBE IT WASN'T REALLY A DREAM.

RAY'S A *TELEPATH.* MAYBE SHE WAS TRYING TO SEND US A MESSAGE?

QUESTION IS, WHY NOW, AFTER STAYING OUT OF TOUCH FOR SO LONG?

AND WHAT'S IT ALL MEAN?

THAT ISN'T FUNNY.

SHOULDN'T WE DO SOMETHING ABOUT IT?

PROBABLY SOME NEW AND TRANSCENDENT DISASTER.

THE PAIR OF US, CRIPPLED AS WE ARE??

JUST 'CAUSE WE'VE BEEN HURT...

...DOESN'T MEAN WE STOP BEING X-MEN.

NOK NOK NOK

CRUMBS, THE DOOR!

DUCK OUTTA SIGHT, KURT...

...WHILE I SEE...

...WHO IT IS?!?

SALUTATIONS, SMALL AND YOUTHFUL SENTIENTS!

Snee. Two paraforms present, mother.

None others close enough to interfere.

I GROW WEARY OF ENDLESSLY REPEATING MYSELF, LIZARD.

DON'T CALL ME MOTHER.

Yes, mother.

→Sigh!←

IF YOU WEREN'T SO INFERNALLY USEFUL...!

I AM GATE-CRASHER.

WOULD YOU PLEASE INFORM THE MASTER OR MISTRESS OF THIS DOMICILE OF MY PRESENCE?

WOULD YOU...

...TAKING YOUR HAND OUTTA MY FACE!

YOU TERRESTRIAL PARAFORMS COME IN SUCH STIMULATINGLY SPIRITED VARIETY.

IT NEVER FAILS TO AMAZE.

LOOK-- GATE-CRASHER-- I HATE TO DISAPPOINT YOU...

...BUT Dr. MacTAGGART-- THIS IS HER HOUSE AND HER ISLAND--

--SHE'S AWAY RIGHT NOW.

IF YOU'D CARE TO LEAVE A NUMBER OR ADDRESS...

REGRETTABLY, DEAR GIRL, TIME OPPRESSES AND DELAYS CANNOT BE COUNTENANCED.

Snee-- mother-- intruder--

--imminently arriving!

18

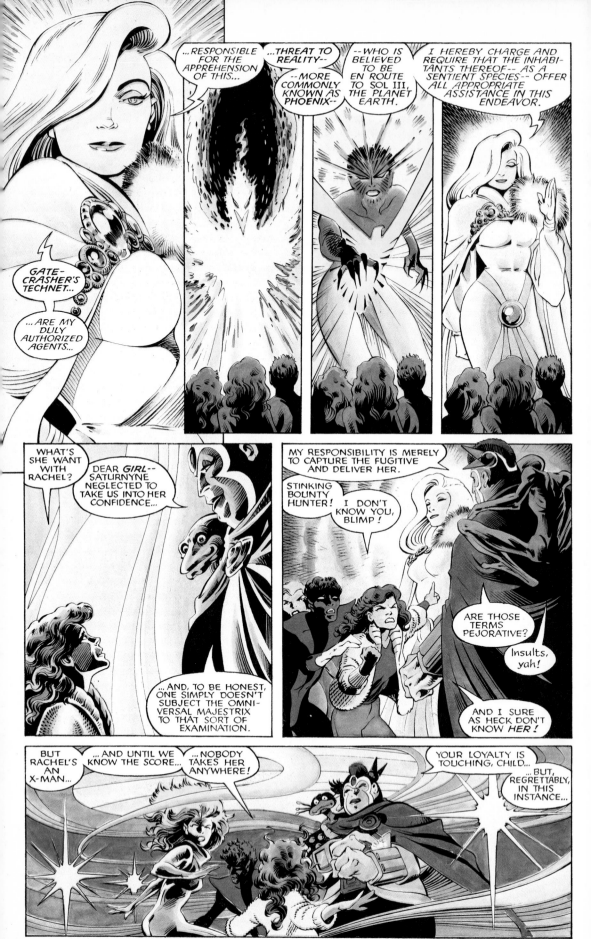

20

SOUNDS LIKE... ...FIGHTING WORDS...

...TO ME!

HAH! CAN'T CATCH, BLIMP-BOYS...

...WHAT YOU CAN'T TOUCH.

WRONG.

Eep!

ADMIRABLE WORK, SCATTERBRAIN.

MEANWHILE...

SPRAY--

--SOME SORT OF TRANSPARENT MEMBRANE--

--COATED ALL OVER-- --CAN'T MOVE--

--POWERS WON'T WORK--

--oh, NO!

GULP

LADIES FIRST.

NOW, YOUNG MAN...

...YOUR TURN.

Pheugkgh!

BAMF

DISAPPEARED, HE DID, GATECRASHER!

A TELE-PORTER.

LIZARD, YOU SHOULD HAVE TOLD ME.

Sorry, Mother.

No scansign of him anywhere close-by.

LET HIM GO. WE'VE GOT MORE IMPORTANT BUSI-NESS TO ATTEND TO.

GATHER UP THE PHASER, BODYBAG--

--WE'LL KEEP THE GIRLS AS BARGAINING CHIPS--

-- AND WE'LL BE ON OUR MERRY WAY.

22

RACHEL SUMMERS.

FALLING

CAST OUT

FLEEING

FROM HEAVEN

HADES NEVER SURE WHICH

ALL THE SAME TO HER--

--SCREAMING CHEERING CRYING...

...WITH JOY AND TERROR COMBINED...

...AS ALL THE COMPONENT ELEMENTS OF HER BEING...

...ARE SHATTERED--

--SPREAD BEYOND REALITY, BEYOND CONCEPTION...

...TO THE FARTHEST REACHES OF CREATION...

...WHERE SPACE HAS NO MEANING, AND TIME EVEN LESS.

FTASZP!

FOR THAT INFINITE MOMENT, SHE IS ALL.

Poit

A MOMENT LATER, SORT OF NOTHING.

AS TRANSCENDENCE GIVES WAY...

...TO REALITY.

Oh!?!

WHAT'S ALL THIS THEN, eh?!

24

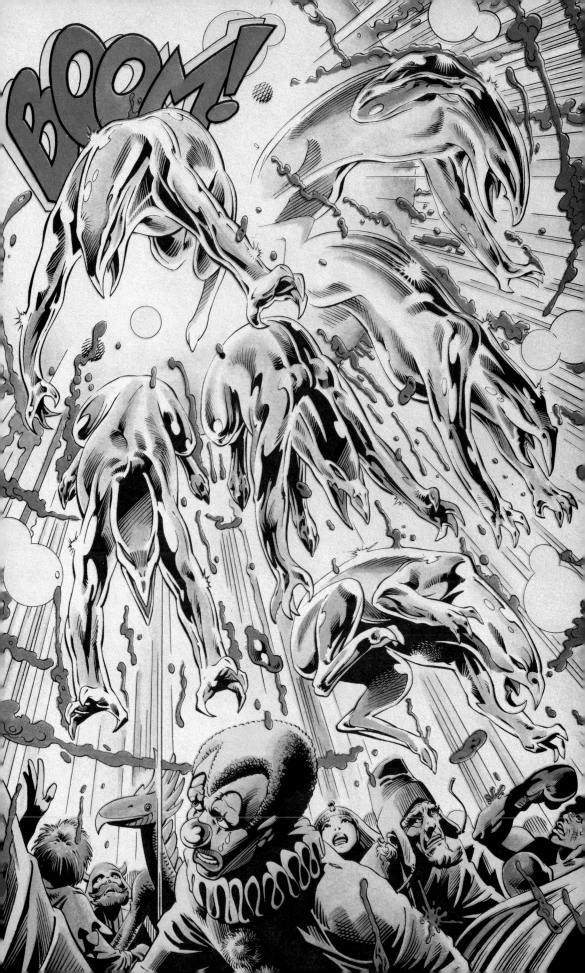

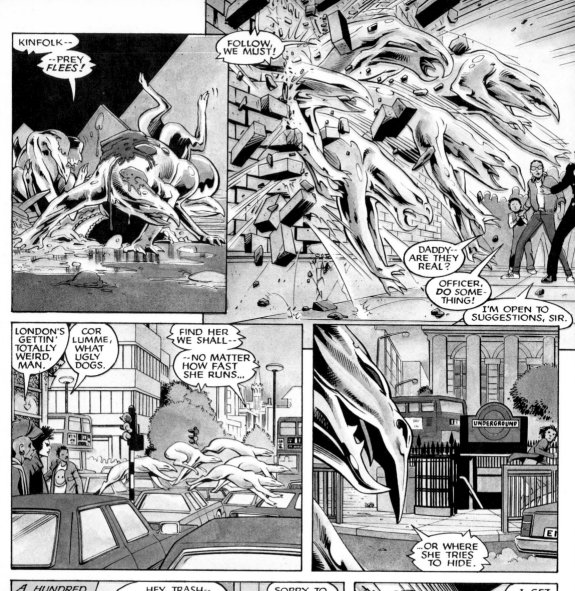

MY ONLY REGRET, BOWSER, IS THAT IT WAS *YOU* I FRIED...

...AND *NOT* YOUR *BLOAT* OF A *BOSS.*

SOMEDAY, THOUGH-- I SWEAR--

--IT'LL BE *HIS* TURN.

Huh?!

THOUGHTS!

SEE HER!

WHAT SHE DID!

LORD HA' MERCY!

MUTIE!

THEY'RE *SO AFRAID.*

OF *ME.*

MONSTER!!

HURT US?

WISH I COULD

RUN AWAY!

HATE HER!

SMASH HER

DO THAT

WITH *GOOD REASON.*

AS RACHEL STRUGGLES TO EXPLAIN, FAILING WITH EVERY WORD...

SNIF

SNUFFLE

SNIF

WHURF

WHIMPER

HOWLOWLO

WLOWLOWLOWW

Gate- crasher-- snee--

--that awful noise.

GIVE IT NO MIND, LIZARD.

MERELY *POOR, DUMB BEASTIES...*

...VENTING THEIR *GRIEF.*

I sense the *starchilde.*

SPLENDID.

WE'VE SPENT QUITE LONG ENOUGH ON THIS *PATHETICALLY PRIMITIVE ORB* ALREADY.

MEANWHILE...

...BACK AT A CERTAIN LIGHTHOUSE...

WHAT A MESS!

AND THE STENCH IS WORSE!

Ach -- EVEN WOLVERINE'S BINGES WERE NEVER AS BAD AS THIS.

WHAT YOU NEED, *HERR KAPITAN*...

...IS A *BATH!*

AND IF PERCHANCE...

...YOU SHOULD FAIL TO RESURFACE--

--WELL, BASED ON WHAT I'VE JUST SEEN...

...NO GREAT LOSS.

However...

BY ALL THE SAINTED DEVILS-- --SOMEONE TRIED TO KILL ME!

HARDLY. YOU'RE DOING WELL ENOUGH ON THAT SCORE BY YOURSELF.

NIGHT-CRAWLER?!

WHAT'S THE MEANING OF THIS?!!

SIMPLE. I NEED YOU AWAKE AND SOBER, AND I'M NOT IN A MOOD TO BE POLITE ABOUT IT.

THAT'S THE EXPLANATION.

IF YOU WISH AN APOLOGY, *HERR BRADDOCK*...

...*EARN* IT!

...BY THE TIME I RETURNED TO THE HOUSE-- AFTER TELEPORTING AWAY-- GATECRASHER WAS LONG GONE. WITH BOTH KITTY AND YOUR *FRAULEIN* MEGGAN.

I DUG UP OUR FILE ON YOU...

...AND SPENT THE REST OF TODAY GETTING HERE.

I NEED YOUR HELP.

I CANNOT TAKE ON THE TECHNET ALONE.

QUITE RIGHT. VERY SENSIBLE. GET ON IT DIRECTLY.

TO BE HONEST, THOUGH, I'M WONDERING IF I MADE A MISTAKE.

WHAT IS *WRONG* WITH YOU, MAN?!

FRIENDS ARE IN DANGER--

--AMONG THEM, THE GIRL YOU SUPPOSEDLY LOVE-- DOESN'T THAT MATTER...

...DON'T YOU *CARE*?!

'COURSE I DO.

IT'S JUST--

--WHAT'S THE POINT?

SAVE THEM NOW TO WATCH THEM SACRIFICE THEM- SELVES LATER.

WE'RE SUPPOSED TO BE HEROES-- BUT WE NEVER REALLY MAKE THINGS BETTER. WE HAVE NO LASTING EFFECT --ON PEOPLE OR THE WORLD.

THE *DEVIL* YOU SAY!

WHEN I SAY I'M A "HERO," I MEAN IT IN JEST. I HAVEN'T THE RIGHT TO TRULY CALL MYSELF ONE. AND YOU HAVE EVEN *LESS* !

ALL I AM IS A MAN, TRYING TO LIVE LIFE AS BEST HE KNOWS HOW, AND BE TRUE TO WHAT HE WAS TAUGHT.

THOSE BELIEFS GOT MY SISTER KILLED !

JA-- AND MY DEAREST FRIENDS WITH HER ! MY "FAMILY" !

MEIN GOTT-- SOME- TIMES, ALL I YEARN FOR, MORE THAN ANYTHING, IS TO HAVE BEEN GIVEN THE CHANCE, THE PRIVI- LEGE, OF STANDING WITH THE X-MEN AND SHARING THEIR FATE !

IT ISN'T FAIR THEY'RE DEAD. IT'S FAR WORSE THAT I REMAIN ALIVE TO GRIEVE FOR THEM, BECAUSE IT'S MORE PAIN THAN I CAN ENDURE !!

BUT *I AM* ALIVE, BRADDOCK !

AND I MUST REMAIN TRUE TO MYSELF, AS TO THEIR MEMORY!

IF THAT IS MORE THAN YOU CAN HANDLE, CAPTAIN BRITAIN...

...I AM SORRY...

...TO HAVE TROUBLED YOU.

YOU DON'T UNDER-STAND!

YOU DON'T KNOW WHAT IT'S LIKE TO ACTUALLY *DIE!*

NO, PERHAPS NOT.

BUT DO YOU, *HERR* BRADDOCK...

...HAVE EVEN THE SLIGHTEST IDEA WHAT IT'S LIKE...

...TO TRULY *LIVE?*

WAIT!

MEMORIES.

YOU BLUE-FURRED GOBLIN, YOU'VE NO RIGHT TO JUDGE ME--!

LYING BROKEN AND BLOODY, MORE RAG DOLL THAN MAN.

WATCHING THE EXECUTIONER'S HAND RISE, THE GUN FLASH...

...SO AFRAID.

AND THEN, WAKING UP.

...BUT NEVER HEALED.

KNOWING DEATH MUST COME AGAIN.

HAUNTED BY THE CERTAINTY...

...THAT THIS TIME WILL TRULY BE THE END.

TERRIFIED BY THE FEAR...

REBORN.

WHOLE...

...THAT IT WON'T.

LONDON

SCROUNGED SOME CLOTHES TO CALL MY OWN.

QUESTION IS, DO I HAVE A PLACE TO GO WITH THEM?

I'M THE PRODIGAL GIRL...

...WHO RAN OUT ON THE X-MEN WHEN THEY NEEDED HER MOST.

Fantasy Fa

Excalibur

I BETRAYED THEIR TRUST.

SERVE ME RIGHT IF THEY SLAM THE DOOR IN MY FACE.

NO SENSE MOPING LOST AND LONELY, SOB-SORRY FOR MYSELF.

THE X-MEN ARE MY FAMILY.

I'VE NOWHERE ELSE TO GASP?!

MALORY'S Morte d'Arthu

SWORD AND THE STONE

EXCALIBUR

KNIGHTS OF THE ROUND TABLE

CAMELOT 3000

THE ONCE AND FUTURE KING

YOU'VE RUN US QUITE A RACE, NAUGHTY STARCHILDE.

BUT IT'S OVER.

SWORD AND THE STONE

BODYBAG, DO THE HONORS!

NO!

NEURAL TOXIN-- INSTANTANEOUSLY INHIBITS THE SYNAPSES, SO NOTHING VOLUNTARY WORKS.

BREATHING'S OKAY, HEARTBEAT, TOO-- ALL THE AUTONOMIC STUFF-- BUT THE MIND GOES FUGUE-BLANK...

...THE BODY REDUCED TO A SACK OF MEAL, TO BE FOLDED ANY WHICH WAY, NO PROBLEM, GOES DOWN SMOOTH AND EASY.

CHOMP

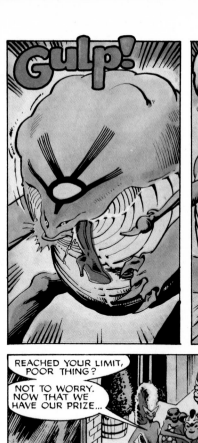

Gulp!

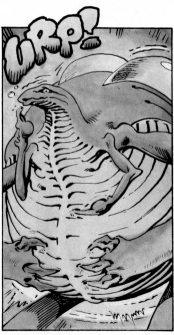

URP!

BLORTCH!

REACHED YOUR LIMIT, POOR THING?

NOT TO WORRY. NOW THAT WE HAVE OUR PRIZE...

...WE CAN DISPENSE WITH THE OTHER TWO.

AND, *NO*, THAT DOES NOT MEAN DINNER.

WE'LL LEAVE THEM HERE.

Ahhh, MY PETS, I DO SO LOVE IT WHEN A CAPER COMES TOGETHER.

Mother--?!?

Trouble!

BLIX!

EXCUSE ME, SENTIENTS--

URRRRK!

--BUT YOU ARE INTERFERING...

...WITH DULY AUTHORIZED REPRESENTATIVES--

--OH, BOTHER!

I NEVER SHOULD HAVE KEPT FERRO ON THE PAYROLL...

...AFTER HIS WARRANTY EXPIRED!

SHAK!

STUPID BEAST--

--HAVE YOU THE SLIGHTEST NOTION...

...HOW INFERNALLY DIFFICULT IT IS...

...TO FIND GOOD HELP!?!

KAK!

YAIE— OWHW!

STOMP!

WHAT A SIGHT! ALMOST A SHAME TO INTERFERE.

BUT THE PRISONERS MIGHT GET HURT IN THE CROSSFIRE!

NICE THING ABOUT RACHEL.

SHE BROADCASTS SUCH A POWERFUL AND DISTINCTIVE BIO-PATTERN...

...THAT THE PORTABLE CEREBRO SENSOR-PACK I BROUGHT WITH ME FROM MUIR ISLE LED ME RIGHT TO HER.

I FIGURED GATECRASHER WOULD CATCH UP SOONER OR LATER.

PITY I DIDN'T HAVE A CHANCE TO WARN RACHEL.

BUT THIS IS MY CHANCE TO MAKE AMENDS.

SWEET DREAMS, BODY-BAG.

KLUD!

NASTY DOGGY! YOU'LL HAVE TO DO FAR BETTER THAN THIS, YOU KNOW...

...TO BEAT ME.

PERFEKT!

SLASSSH!

37

BEASTIES-- SO SLEEK AND SHINY--

--LOVE THE WAY LIGHT SPLASHES ON SILVER SKIN--

--THEY DON'T APPROVE, OUR TAKING PHOENIX.

NAUGHTY, NAUGHTY-- SHE'S OUR PRIZE!

AS YOU BECOME MINE!

BUT TOO BIG AND WRIGGLY YOU ARE.

SO CHINA DOLL WILL SHRINK YOU... ...TO A PRETTIER SIZE.

YIPE?!

WEAR YOU, SHALL I, AS A GLITTER-BANGLE!

FEEL SO SLIMY, INSIDE AND OUT.

POOR HEAD ACHES-- BRIAN!

IN TROUBLE!!

I'LL HELP YOU, MY LO-- HH!?!

THIS IS WAXWORKS.

THE MEREST TOUCH...

...AND THE BODY LOSES ALL FIRMNESS.

GAHYH!

MEGGAN!

SO DECENT A MAN.

SO EASILY-- FATALLY-- DISTRACTED...

...BY CONCERN FOR THOSE HE CARES ABOUT.

A MOMENTARY THING...

...THAT SCATTERBRAIN TURNS INTO AN ETERNITY...

Gklk!

...AS HER CARESS FIRES ALL HIS NEURAL SYNAPSES AT ONCE...

THAT'S THE SPIRIT--

--TIDE'S TURNING!

... ON YOUR BOSS!

HERE, DOLL-FACE--

--WORK YOUR MINIATURIZING MAGIC...

Oh DEAR oh DEAR oh DEAR

SLITHERING BUFFOON-- SEE WHAT YOU'VE DONE TO ME!

THAT'S NOTHING, BLIMP--

Eh?

--COMPARED TO WHAT I'M GOING TO DO!

TAKING ALL MY CONCENTRA-TION TO STAY SOLID--

--BOD'LL HURT TOMORROW FROM THE STRAIN--

--BUT, BOY, IS THIS WORTH IT!

SOK!

YOU-- YOU-- YOU--!

HIT YOU. HARD AS I COULD. CARE FOR AN ENCORE?!

YAP!

ENOUGH!!

AWAY!!!

THEY'RE VANISHING!

TELEPORTING!

THEN WE WON!

GOOD RIDDANCE!

THE WARWOLVES--?!

GONE, AS WELL-- --PREFERING DISCRETION, THE BETTER PART OF VALOR-- --TO LICK WOUNDS, MOURN LOST COMRADES, REGAIN STRENGTH... ...AND PLAN FOR ANOTHER CHASE, A HAPPIER DAY.

ANOTHER NIGHT...

... (AFTER THE MESS IN LONDON HAS BEEN TIDIED UP...

... AND EXPLANATIONS MADE TO THE APPROPRIATE AUTHORITIES)...

... ATOP THE SCOTS HIGHLANDS.

Oh, NIGHTCRAWLER, I'D GIVE ANYTHING... ...TO HAVE SEEN THAT!

IT WAS AN EXPERIENCE.

AND THOSE WERE THE DAYS.

YOUR TURN, RACHEL.

...SO PROFESSOR XAVIER SPENDS *WEEKS* PROGRAMMING THE DANGER ROOM FOR MY TRIAL SESSION...

...AND I WALK THROUGH IT UNTOUCHED...

...WITH MY EYES CLOSED!

ANY MEMORIES OF THE X-MEN...

...YOU'D CARE TO SHARE?

WOLVERINE CHALLENGED ME...

...TO WALK DOWN THE MAIN STREET OF SALEM CENTER...

...UNDISGUISED, IN MY NATURAL SHAPE.

NOT THE KIND YOU MEAN, KITTY.

NOT THE KIND I CAN TRUST.

THE FACTS IN MY HEAD, THEY'RE SO JUMBLED UP...

... I DON'T KNOW ANY-MORE WHAT'S REAL AND WHAT ISN'T--

--WHAT ACTUALLY HAPPENED...

...WHAT'S A LIE.

44

BUT THAT DOESN'T MATTER.

BECAUSE THE CLUTTER DOESN'T AFFECT MY EMOTIONAL REALITIES-- PERHAPS, IN TURN, BECAUSE THE PHOENIX BY NATURE RELATES, RESPONDS BETTER TO FEELINGS THAN RATIONALITY.

I KNOW WHO *I* AM--

--WHO I CARE FOR, WHO I DON'T-- THAT'S WHAT MATTERS.

THE REST, I CAN TAKE OR LEAVE.

SPEAKING OF LEAVING...

...IT'S AWFULLY LATE. TIME, I THINK, TO FOLLOW EVERYBODY ELSE'S EXAMPLE...

...AND RETURN HOME TO BED.

IS THAT IT?!

PACK UP, CALL THINGS QUITS...

...AND GO OUR SEPARATE WAYS?!!

WE ACCOMPLISHED WHAT WE SET OUT TO DO. NOW, WHILE I DEAL WITH THE WARWOLVES...

...THE REST OF YOU CAN GO ON WITH YOUR LIVES.

WHAT ABOUT THOSE LIVES--

--HOW ARE WE SUPPOSED TO LIVE THEM?!

I DON'T UNDERSTAND, RACHEL, WHAT DO YOU MEAN?!

THE *DREAM*, CAPTAIN-- CHARLES XAVIER'S DREAM-- OF A WORLD WHERE *ALL* EARTH'S CHILDREN, MUTANT AND OTHERWISE, LIVE TOGETHER IN PEACE AND HARMONY!

WHERE PEOPLE ARE JUDGED FOR WHO THEY *ARE*-- NOT WHAT THEY LOOK LIKE OR HOW THEY'RE BORN.

THAT'S WHY HE CREATED THE *X-MEN*, TO EXEMPLIFY THAT DREAM.

ARE YOU SAYING, SIMPLY BECAUSE THE X-MEN ARE DEAD...

...WE'RE SUPPOSED TO GIVE IT UP?!

45

THE DREAM *WE* HAD, NIGHT-CRAWLER-- REMEMBER, BACK BEFORE THIS CRAZY CAPER BEGAN -- IN IT, RACHEL SAID TO ME:

"...WHEN THE REALITY NO LONGER EXISTS, EXPLOITERS CAN TAKE THE LEGEND...

"... AND MAKE IT WHATEVER THEY WANT...

"... GOOD OR BAD."

ARE YOU SUGGESTING WE TAKE THE X-MEN'S PLACE?

NOBODY CAN DO THAT. BUT *KING ARTHUR* HAD A DREAM, TOO.

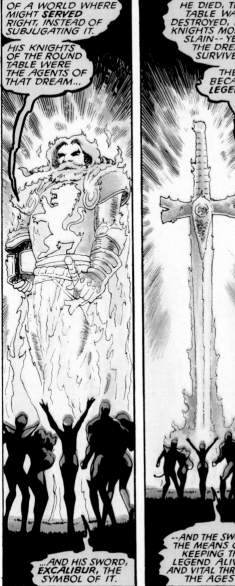

OF A WORLD WHERE MIGHT *SERVED* RIGHT, INSTEAD OF SUBJUGATING IT.

HIS KNIGHTS OF THE ROUND TABLE WERE THE AGENTS OF THAT DREAM...

...AND HIS SWORD, *EXCALIBUR,* THE SYMBOL OF IT.

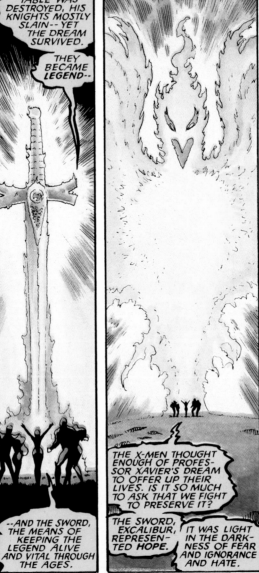

HE DIED, THE TABLE WAS DESTROYED, HIS KNIGHTS MOSTLY SLAIN-- YET THE DREAM SURVIVED.

THEY BECAME *LEGEND*--

--AND THE SWORD, THE MEANS OF KEEPING THE LEGEND ALIVE AND VITAL THROUGH THE AGES.

THE X-MEN THOUGHT ENOUGH OF PROFESSOR XAVIER'S DREAM TO OFFER UP THEIR LIVES. IS IT SO MUCH TO ASK THAT WE FIGHT TO PRESERVE IT?

THE SWORD, EXCALIBUR, REPRESEN-TED HOPE.

IT WAS LIGHT IN THE DARK-NESS OF FEAR AND IGNORANCE AND HATE.

DO WE WANT--

--HAVE WE THE RIGHT--

--TO SNUFF IT OUT?